Fun with

Sizes

🌸 Belitha Press

First published in the UK in 1998 by

Belitha Press Limited,
London House, Great Eastern Wharf,
Parkgate Road, London SW11 4NQ

This edition first published in 1999
Reprinted 1999

ISBN 1 85561 849 4 (paperback)
ISBN 1 85561 771 4 (hardback)

British Library Cataloguing in Publication Data
for this book is available from the British Library.

Printed in Hong Kong

Series editor: Honor Head
Series designer: Jamie Asher
Illustrator: Kirsty Asher

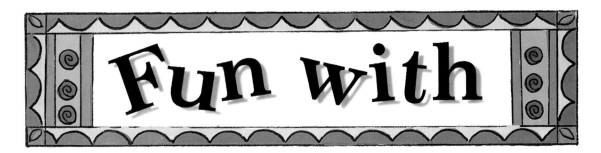

Sizes

written by
Peter Patilla

illustrated by
Kirsty Asher

About this book

Fun with Sizes will help children to grasp the important concept of size. The puzzles will encourage them to learn words which will help them to express size differences. The games and puzzles have been created to show the difference between size opposites, such as thick and thin and big and small. Size comparisons, such as longer and shorter and small, medium and big, and objects which are the same size, are also introduced.

Confident children will enjoy tackling the puzzles on their own. Help less confident children by going through the book with them and talking about each puzzle before they begin to solve it. The puzzles can be done in any order and at a pace which suits the children. If the children give a wrong answer, explain why it is wrong and encourage them to start again.

Contents

The Three Bears

Match the small, medium and big spoon, plate, honey pot, bowl and mug to each bear.

small

medium

big

Long and Short

Which caterpillar is the longest?
Which spider has the shortest thread?

Wild Tracks

Find the small, medium and big footprints...

 for the lizard

 for the frog

 for the bird

Two of a Kind

Match the pictures below with ones the same size in the picture opposite.

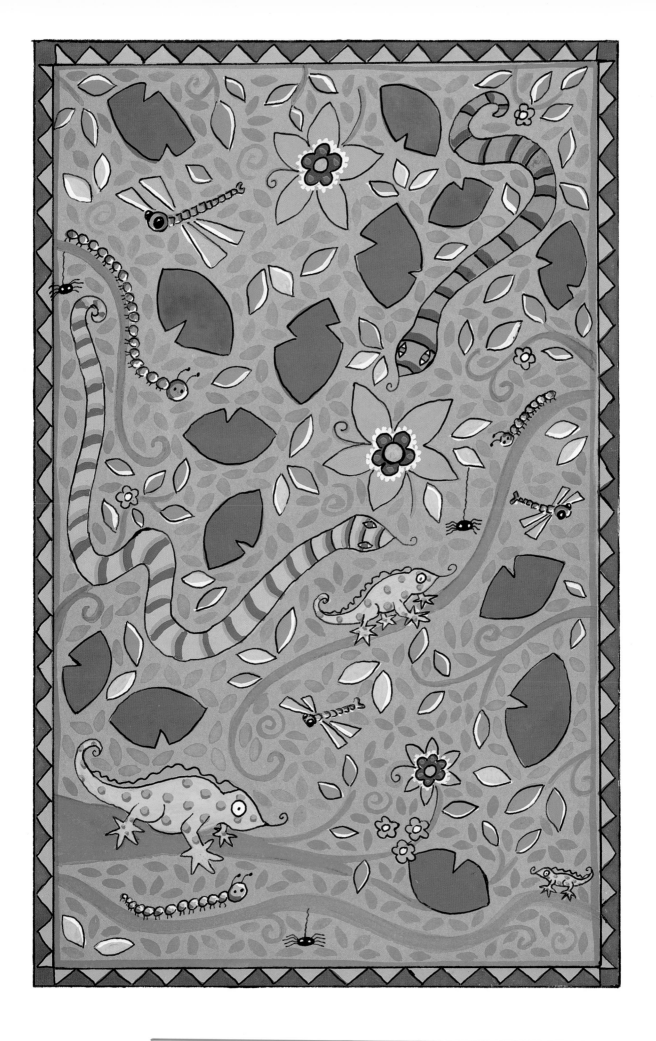

Leap Frog

Whose jump was the longest?
Whose jump was the shortest?

Which frog has jumped the highest?

Picking Coconuts

Which ladder do you need to reach the coconuts on each tree?

Flower Vases

Which flowers fit in each vase?

Flower Chains

Which flower chain is the longest?

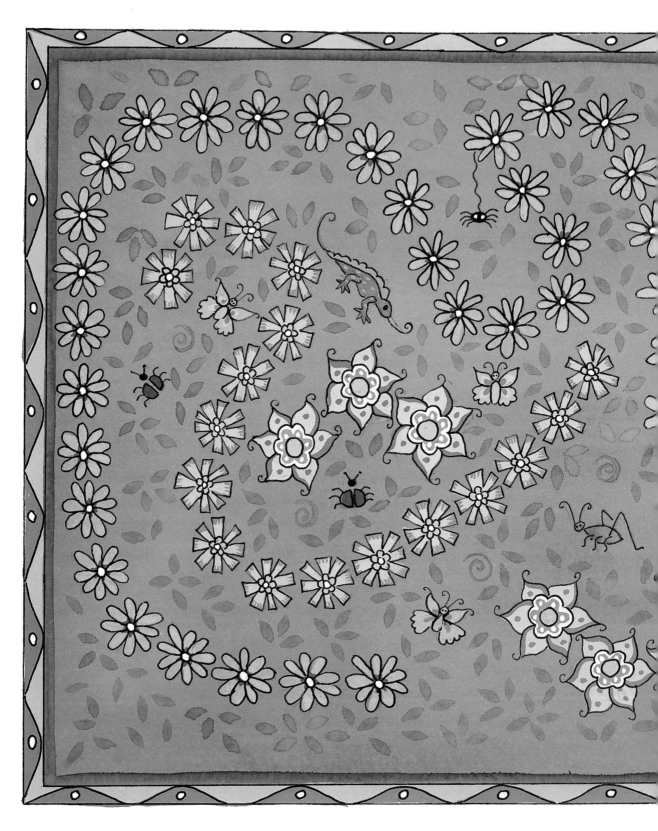

Which flower chains are shorter than the white one?

Log Cabin

Find the thinnest and the thickest log in the log cabin.

thin log   thick log

Match the logs to the trees below.

Snake Pit

Can you find the longest snake?
Can you find the shortest snake?

Fish Scales

Find the fish the same size as these.

On the Shelf

Find the tallest bottle on each shelf. Can you find the widest bottle and the smallest bottle on the shelves?

In the picture opposite can you find...

shorter flower chains than this?

thicker vines than this?

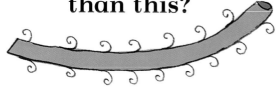

shorter caterpillars than this?

taller flowers than this?

smaller birds than this?

Sizes

long   short

tall

thick   thin

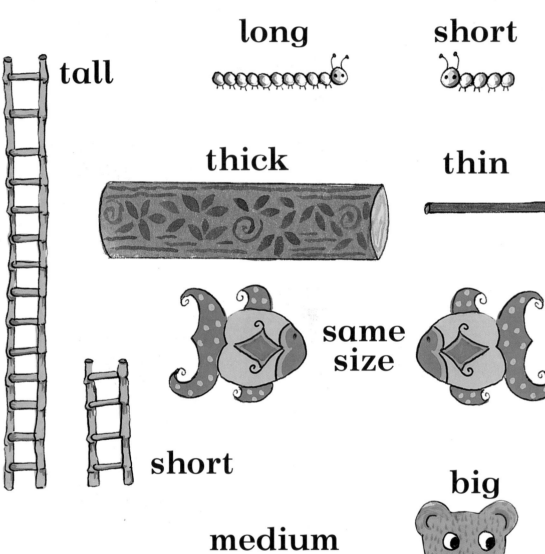

same size

short

big

medium

small